DIARY OF A DISCIPLE:

LUKE'S STORY

ACTIVITY BOOK

Gemma Willis

Illustrated by Emma Randall

you absolutely *SHOULD*, and you'll probably find it

pretty tricky to solve the **puzzles** if you don't.

And actually, wherever there is a LITTLE bit of white space

— colour it in! Make this book your (own) — decorate it, draw

in it, colour it, **ENJOY** it! Now — I don't know if you

know, but this book is actually a tiny, weeny mini-version

of my | sto | ry. | I've tried to pick out all the bits you

need to see how the story goes, but if you want to know more,

if you want to hear the (whole) story, you can read it here:

OH, and did you know that (my) story,

the story in this **puzzle** book, can be

found in the Bible itself (but without the puzzles!)? The

Bible is just a ✝ **BIG** collection of books that

DIARY OF DISCIPLE

tell God's **BIG** 📖 story — and (my) story is just a little

part of his even bigger story! That's super awesome — right?

Anyway — I **GUESS** it's over to you now and

I'll be there to talk you through it as we go...

👀
Look, here's a bit ➡️ [   ] of that white space I was

talking about — colour it in! Maybe you could draw a picture

of **YOU** reading this book and using your thinky, puzzly brain...

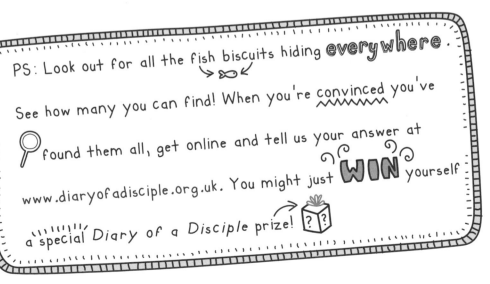

PS: Look out for all the fish biscuits hiding **everywhere**.

See how many you can find! When you're convinced you've

🔍 found them all, get online and tell us your answer at

www.diaryofadisciple.org.uk. You might just **WIN** yourself

a special *Diary of a Disciple* prize! ❓❓

WHO **IS LUKE?**

START

Singer
Luke

SO now you know, Luke was a 🩺. You know, the kind that makes 😟→🙂 when they're 🤒. But, he also did some other ⭐ things. He wrote an entire 📖 — well 2 actually because he had something really, really ‼️ that he wanted to 🤲 with the whole 🌍.

6

Farmer Luke

Carpenter Luke

Chef Luke

Doctor Luke

Camel Keeper Luke

Shepherd Luke

7

Where did **LUKE'S** story start?

World-changing stories usually start with something **BIG**, but this one starts with something super small. Colour in this awesome picture and, as you do, you'll find *everything* has a matching pair — all except (one) very [TINY] thing. And it's this [TINY] thing that was the start of the most **AMAZING** story **EVER**!

How can a BABY change the world?

Have a LOOK at the crowd below — five of them are telling us things that Dr Luke wanted us to know, five of them aren't. Colour in the people who are telling the TRUTH.

This **BABY** had a **SPECIAL** name.

Here are a **few facts** about that name
— can **YOU** piece them back together?

in a big book called the Bible

An angel told his parents that

His name means 'God saves',

His name is a **HEBREW**

reason it was given to him , and had an $

hundreds of times

in the middle...

unusual name — but the

name **hundreds**

, and ended in

12

name

was *pretty* special!

they **HAD** to give him this

version of JOSHUA

It wasn't an

You can (find) his

It started with a

 SO what **WAS** his name?

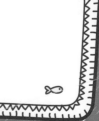

WHY was he SO SPECIAL?

He was a <u>normal</u> **BABY**, but a super special baby — because he was actually **GOD**! Woah... Maybe I should try and explain...

Are you ready?

1 God the **FATHER** is God. He made everything, he is everywhere, he has **always** been there and will be there for ever.

2 **JESUS** is God. He's God's Son — God in **heaven** (sometimes called "Father" or "Daddy") decided to send Jesus to **earth** to live as a human being like **you** and **me**.

3 The **HOLY SPIRIT** is God. We haven't mentioned him yet. He's **AWESOME**! He guides people who **believe** in God and does super <u>cool</u> things.

Sounds **WEIRD**, I know, but this might <u>help</u>...

This is an **ORANGE**. (Obviously!) There are three things about this orange that are <u>true</u>:

This orange is 100% a fruit. It's <u>still</u> totally an orange.

This orange is 100% orange coloured. It's <u>still</u> totally an orange.

This orange is 100% round. It's <u>still</u> totally an orange.

This orange is **ALL** these things — but it's still (one) orange, **right**? That's kind of how this God thing works.

The Father is 100% the Father. He's also **TOTALLY** God.

Jesus is 100% Jesus. He's also **TOTALLY** God.

The Holy Spirit is 100% the Holy Spirit. He's also **TOTALLY** God.

Did that <u>help</u>? **Anyway**... I should also say that God *DEFINITELY* isn't an orange.

15

One of the FIRST super AWESOME things

that Jesus did was disappear! Literally — one minute he

was there; the next minute he was GONE!

Some people that he'd been talking to decided they

didn't (like) him so much and made a plan to throw him off

a cliff — nice! They grabbed Jesus and kicked him out of

Nazareth and then they chased him like a swarm of

angry wasps right to the edge of a cliff. They were

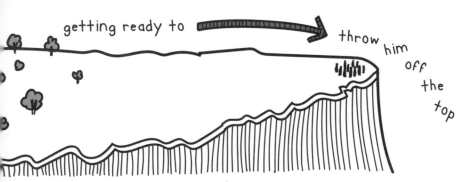

getting ready to ➡ throw him off the top

when they SUDDENLY couldn't find him.

Another SUPER AWESOME thing involved fish. LOTS of them.

SOME of Jesus' friends were fishermen, and they spent all night, every night, trying to catch fish — I mean, that's what a fisherman does, right?

Simon was one of those fishermen, and he wasn't having a very good fishy time. IN FACT, he'd been out all night trying to catch fish and hadn't caught a single one. IN FACT, he was convinced that ALL the fish had disappeared. He normally caught a few, but this time he'd only managed to drag up the odd ROCK and a few STINKY old sandals.

But when Jesus (told) Simon where to drop the nets, guess what? There were LOADS and LOADS and LOADS of (fish.) There were SOOOOOO many that the fishing nets started to RIP!

How many fish can you SQUEEZE into Simon's nets? Draw as <u>many</u> as you can!

Fill in the crossword below to discover **lots** of things that are **really** important in the next super awesome story!

Across

2 Holding something while you move along (8)

6 Opposite of woman (3)

7 Opposite of below (5)

8 Saying something very loudly (8)

9 What you are after you've been made better (6)

10 Like a rug, but for snuggling under (7)

Down

1 Using your feet to move along slowly (4)

2 A large group of people in one place (5)

3 Pieces of clay or other material used to make a roof (5)

4 Unexpected, awesome (7)

5 Choosing not to hold a grudge (13)

6 The noise of a crowd all talking quietly at once (9)

Now you've figured **OUT** the words, can **YOU** work out where they go in this **AMAZING** story?

Some people were c _ _ r y _ _ _ a man on a blanket, because he couldn't _ _ _ k . They wanted him to be _ _ _ _ l e _ by Jesus, but they couldn't get through the busy, s _ _ _ t _ _ _ _ _ _ w _ . Then one of them had an (idea.) He climbed up on the roof and started pulling off the _ _ _ l _ _ . Everyone inside stared up at him. Then a (bulging) blanket began to come down slowly from a b _ _ _ through the hole. When it **FINALLY** arrived on the floor, it unfolded to (reveal) a _ _ n lying there.

Jesus smiled and said, "My friend, you have f _ _ g i _ _ _ _ _ _ _ ." The crowd started _ u t _ _ _ i _ _ . "Go on," said Jesus, "get up, take your _ l _ _ k _ _ and walk home." A _ z _ _ _ !

21

Check out this story, about Jesus and a Roman officer's servant, and then SEE if you can travel all the way from Jesus to the sick servant in his bed!

There was a Roman officer (I'm going to call him Jim because I can't remember his proper Roman name) who had a servant who was really, really sick. IN FACT, he was probably going to die pretty quickly if nothing changed.

Jim had heard all about JESUS and he asked some of his Jewish friends to go and find Jesus and ask him to come and heal his servant. So, when they found him, Jesus went with Jim's friends, and when he was nearly there Jim sent some people out to meet him with a message.

"Don't come all the way to my HOUSE, Jesus, I'm nowhere

NEAR good enough to have you in my house. But I know that if you just *say so* then my servant will be better again."

Jesus was SERIOUSLY impressed. "I've never seen someone with this much *faith* — and he's a Roman!"

Jim's friends went **BACK** to his house and the servant was up and about — looking BETTER than ever! He didn't look anywhere near dead!

One day, Jesus and his mates were on a boat, and Jesus decided he wanted to cross **L**ake **G**alilee.

While Jesus was **snoozing** everything went dark. The wind was howling and the boat started to fill with water.

His mates "**SHOOK**" him awake — "We're going to die! **HELP!**" "Oi! Jesus — wake up!"

Jesus opened his eyes, *stretched* and stood up. He looked around at the storm and said, "**STOP**, waves, **STOP**, wind," and then sat back down again as the waves and wind **calmed** down. Then he said, "Haven't you got **ANY** *faith*?"

I think the disciples must've been pretty "scared".

JESUS was in control all along — he wanted

his mates to learn to trust him. How do you feel about

trusting Jesus?

How **many** of the "being scared" words can you find in this wordsearch?

Freaked Out

Shaky   Unsure

Uncertain

Afraid   Nervous

Worried

Scared   Wobbly

Frightened

Terrified

x	f	e	h	k	o	a	p	l	n	t	u	i	x	c
a	t	e	r	r	i	f	i	e	d	d	f	t	y	j
r	t	g	d	s	v	r	r	w	e	f	j	u	l	d
r	t	h	f	a	w	a	u	k	j	y	t	f	e	t
c	g	j	b	f	y	i	t	r	h	k	i	n	y	h
w	s	c	a	r	e	d	b	g	r	e	e	e	j	h
t	h	y	r	e	t	r	g	c	d	t	s	r	k	m
r	a	f	d	a	p	u	j	n	h	i	s	v	e	d
v	k	o	m	k	o	s	f	g	w	v	j	o	m	p
w	y	l	b	e	d	e	i	r	r	o	w	u	s	e
z	x	t	y	d	n	r	c	s	e	i	o	s	c	h
p	o	u	k	o	f	t	e	a	d	f	b	j	y	k
m	z	r	f	u	n	s	u	r	e	g	b	j	y	k
a	x	t	y	t	e	j	y	u	o	l	l	e	j	v
i	n	i	a	t	r	e	c	n	u	p	y	r	r	t

Jesus met a man called Jairus who had a very, very poorly daughter. She was dying. Jairus begged Jesus to come and SEE her, but Jesus kept getting stopped along the way.

Jairus was waiting and waiting for Jesus to come (with) him.

Then his WORST fears were realised when he saw someone from his HOUSE running towards them. "She's DIED. She's gone. Don't bother him any more."

But Jesus said, "DON'T worry, Jairus. It's OK. Have faith and she'll be well again."

When they arrived at Jairus' house everyone was crying. Great big soggy tears and super LOUD waily sobs.

"She's **NOT** dead, she's just asleep," said Jesus.

Everyone "LAUGHED" at Jesus. They must've thought he was a little bit stupid — clearly she was very dead! DUH!

But then, Jesus **held** the little girl's hand and said, "Get up!"

And right before their eyes she **STOOD** up, alive and well.

Can you spot 1 big and 9 small differences in these pictures?

27

ONE time, there was a **CROWD** of thousands and thousands of people *listening* to Jesus — and they stayed for **SOOOO** *long* it was starting to get dark! The disciples were worried — all these people had "rumbly" tummies.

"**YOU** sort them out," said Jesus.

"But we only have **five** bread rolls and **two** skinny fish. We'd have to spend a **FORTUNE** just to get a mouthful for each of them."

Jesus picked up the bread (rolls) and the skinny (fish) and looked up towards **HEAVEN**. He said a prayer and then he *PULLED* the rolls apart and broke up the fish and gave it to his mates. "**GO** and share this out," he said.

The entire crowd ate as **much** as they possibly could, and even then they ended up with baskets of leftovers — and not just **manky** fish bones and bread crumbs, but **PROPER**, tasty leftovers. **WOW**! How did **THAT** happen? Just look at all those people! Jesus fed them all with just **5** loaves and **2** fish — and they had *LEFTOVERS*.

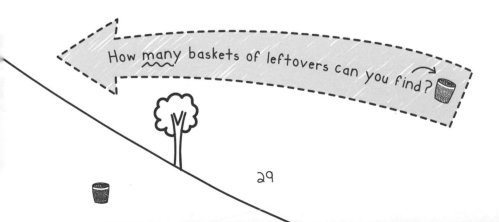

How <u>many</u> baskets of leftovers can you find?

As well as doing really **AMAZING** stuff, Jesus said some absolutely mind-blowing things, too. He also chose **12** people to be his **SPECIAL** followers. They went **everywhere** with him and tried to learn <u>as much</u> as they **COULD** from him. But can you **WORK OUT** who is who using the information below? I've filled in a few names to get you started! Here they are:

Andrew has **2** thick black stripes on <u>each</u> shoulder.

James 2, Matthew and John don't have a beard. ✗

Prayer is just a *fancy* word for talking to GOD. And Jesus taught his disciples one really

AWESOME prayer!

See if YOU can fill in the <u>missing</u> words!

"DAD, in ☁ _____ , please help us to ⓜ _____ how ☆ _____ you are. Let what YOU ♡ _____ happen here on 🌍 _____ . Provide for us every day ↻ _____ that we 🐟 _____ and please ✋ _____ us when we do ✗ _____ . Help us to ✋ _____ others who do wrong to us, too, and help us NOT to be 〰 _____ into things that are NO ☺ _____ ."

remember ⓜ   forgive ✋   wrong ✗   good ☺   everything ↻

earth 🌍   need 🐟   lured 〰   awesome ☆   Heaven ☁   want ♡

People who *follow* Jesus pray lots. They talk to GOD about all kinds of things. Can you find all the things Jesus' followers **often** pray about hidden in this wordsearch? When you've found them *ALL*, the remaining letters will SPELL OUT what Jesus said his *followers* could always talk to GOD about...

N	S	D	N	E	I	R	F	C
A	S	W	F	U	N	I	S	L
T	S	P	O	R	A	A	A	O
U	E	E	Y	R	A	B	D	T
R	N	O	I	U	K	S	N	H
E	L	T	E	R	V	C	E	E
S	L	D	E	R	R	H	S	S
T	I	O	Y	T	H	O	S	M
E	J	O	Y	S	I	O	W	E
P	N	F	A	M	I	L	Y	G

Friends   School

Family   Sadness

Nature   Work

Pets   Illness

Food   Worries

Clothes   Joys

Air   Fun   Me

(Not "me" as in Dr Luke — but you! Jesus' followers __often__ pray for themselves — just like Jesus did.)

SO, like I said before, one of the **reasons** why Jesus came to *earth* was to tell **everyone** how much God loves them. God had been trying to tell people this from the beginning of **TIME**, but they didn't always do a very good job of *listening*. So this time God sent his **OWN** Son to deliver the message!

But **JESUS'** message wasn't *JUST* about God loving (us), it was an invitation for (us) to love God **BACK**.

"Love God with **everything** you are and *love* your neighbour as much as you *love* yourself."

Find out which **AREA** the people God *loves* live in.

Join up the dots!

But you SEE, the THING (is,) people don't always love GOD back — at least not ALL the time. I know I don't! Jesus' *followers* call not loving God "sin".

It's QUITE easy to imagine that "sin" is about breaking the rules — but that's not it AT ALL. It's about BREAKING GOD'S heart. I know that sounds a bit EXTREME — but honestly, it's <u>true</u>.

OK — let me try and explain. You have a pet dog. He's *lovely* and you're so "excited" to be his friend. Your dog knows he's only supposed to poop outside. <u>Most</u> of the time that's what he does.

36

But ONE day, he poops on the white rug in your HOUSE

— while you're standing right NEXT to him! You can't quite

believe what he's done — but he needs to **understand**

that pooping on the rug just is not OK. So he ends up outside,

in the doghouse. But now he's

outside and you're inside

feeling SAD without

him. If you go and get

him, then he'll (think) pooping

on the rug is *fine*, but you really miss him. You're

heartbroken that he's separated from you...

That's kind of how GOD feels when WE sin. But that's

why he sent JESUS.

Anyway. We'll come ◄back to the doghouse thing in a bit.

In the MEANTIME — I want to tell you about

SOME of the things Jesus __said__ about how people who *follow*

him should LIVE.

"If people say HORRIBLE things to you, ask

God to *bless* them. If people are harsh with you, then

pray for them. If someone wants to take your coat, then

let him have your shirt too. If someone asks, always give

and don't ask for it back. In fact, if you think about it,

it's SIMPLE — how would __you__ like to be treated?

Then be like that with everyone.

38

"It's **easy** to be nice to people who are nice to you.

No, if you really *love* God then be different.

Really love your enemies; God loves them, you know. He has

good things for everyone, even the people you DON'T LIKE!

And let's face it, you're not PERFECT

either — and God still

LOVES

YOU!"

Can you decipher God's SPECIAL message to you?

God **really, really** loves you just as you are. There's

NOTHING you could do to make him love you MORE

and there's NOTHING you could do to make him love you less.

JESUS was a *pretty* clever guy, you know. Just listen to what he said **NEXT**:

"People are a bit like trees. If they're **GOOD** on the inside, then their fruit is good, too, but if they're **BAD** on the inside, their fruit will **ALWAYS** be bad. With trees you can tell if they're good or not by the way their fruit tastes. People are just the same. You can **ALWAYS** tell by what someone says and does what they're really like on the -inside:-

How **many** words can you find in this wordsearch that would be like **GOOD** fruit in someone's life? There are a few "bad" ones in there, too — so watch out!

x	c	f	t	y	j	k	o	p	d	e
k	i	n	d	n	e	s	s	m	g	s
f	r	t	e	a	u	p	o	e	h	s
v	e	t	z	f	d	g	h	a	k	e
o	a	g	s	h	a	r	i	n	g	n
h	t	f	i	g	h	t	i	n	g	e
k	p	e	c	v	b	e	g	e	u	v
g	i	v	i	n	g	s	l	s	m	i
j	y	o	j	b	u	v	p	s	c	g
l	t	l	c	e	s	x	h	s	e	r
e	c	n	e	i	t	a	p	v	x	o
f	j	t	y	u	i	s	e	k	l	f

Write all the "good fruit" words you can find here:

41

Not everyone LIKED Jesus all that much. Some people thought he was a troublemaker who was just trying to cause ARGUMENTS and *PROBLEMS* — because he was telling people to do things differently than they'd been done for hundreds and hundreds of years.

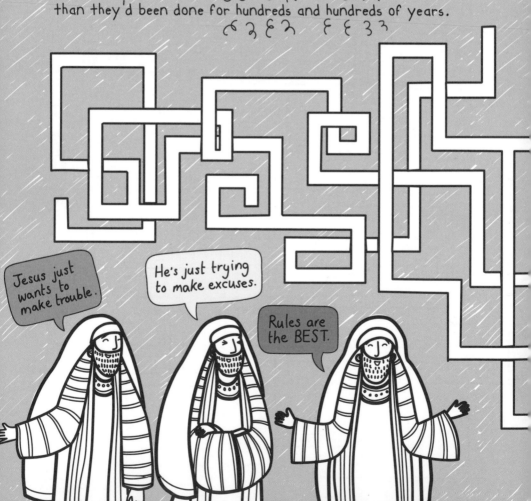

The people in charge in Jerusalem decided the ONLY way they could stop Jesus from causing trouble was to catch him, arrest him and make him go away. For ever.

They wanted to arrest Jesus, but they were proper scared of what the crowds might do. They kept a CLOSE eye on him, looking for every opportunity they could to make him SAY or DO something they could ARREST him for. They wanted to hand him over to the Roman leaders, so they hatched a dirty, sneaky LITTLE plan. They sent some men to ask Jesus a question that would catch him out. They reckoned their plan was totally foolproof, THIS time.

Two of these Pharisees were <u>involved</u> in hatching the **dirty**, *sneaky* LITTLE plan. Can you SEE which ones they are? ([Hint] – they're the **ONLY** two who <u>don't have</u> a **matching** pair.)

WELL. They didn't catch him <u>that</u> time – but they decided to hatch **another** *sneaky* LITTLE plan.

Anyway. Jesus and his mates were about to have a <u>very</u> special meal together. It was called the "PASSOVER" meal. Can YOU put the pieces of this scroll together to FIND OUT what they were celebrating?

ating Passover for
have been getting ready
...is a Jewish festival. So

...their ve...
...gypt. You can
...have one – have a look a...

(The Passo-
every Jew in
to celebrate it. The

HAT? Passover
erusalem would'v...
ey'd been celebra...
ds of years by havi...
when th...

hundreds and hundre...
that reminded them of...
was set free from...
Bible, if you...

...ing a special meal
y ancient family
read all about it in the
+ Exodus chapter 12.)

Just BEFORE they were about to tuck in, Jesus said:

I've been **really** looking forward to having this meal with you guys before everything starts to **HAPPEN**. I'm going to **suffer** soon and I won't get to have a meal like **THIS** until we're all together with **GOD**.

Then Jesus picked up some of the bread from the table and *thanked* God for that, too. He **tore** the bread into pieces and gave it to the disciples and said: "This bread is my **BODY**. It is BROKEN for you. Eat it as a way of remembering me."

He picked up **another** cup of wine, thanked **GOD** for it and said: "This wine is my **blood**. It is poured out for **YOU**. God is using it to make **everything NEW**."

Then it all got seriously  **WEIRD.**

Jesus looked **EACH** of the disciples in the eye and said,

"The person who is going to **BETRAY** me is here, in

this room: it's one of you. I will die just as I was **meant**

to, but for the person who betrays me it will be horrible.

Everything went **CRAZY**. The disciples started fighting

with each other, trying to find out who would **EVER**

BETRAY Jesus.

It's **NOT** me!

I would never do that!

Is it you?

What's he talking about, he can't suffer?!!

The disciples **carried on** fighting and ended up arguing

about who was the **BEST**.

Can YOU fill in the missing words in this puzzle using the clues below? When you've ~finished~, the name of the person who betrayed Jesus will be spelled out in the blue squares.

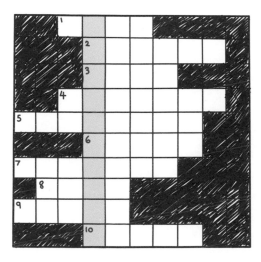

1 Jesus fed thousands of people with five loaves and two of these! (4) (p28 and p29)

2 The number of men Jesus chose to follow him (6) (p30 and p31)

3 The drink Jesus just shared with his friends (4) (p46 and p47)

4 One of Jesus' mates whose name has seven letters (7) (p30 and p31)

5 The thing Jesus and his mates were celebrating (8) (p46 and p47)

6 One of Jesus' mates whose name has an 'M' in the middle and ends in an 'S' (5) (p30 and p31)

7 What the people who didn't like Jesus said he was causing (7) (p44 and p45)

8 When Jesus tore the food and gave it to his friends he said, "This is my ____" (4) (p46 and p47)

9 The food Jesus just shared with his friends (5) (p46 and p47)

10 The thing that Jesus calmed when he was in a boat with his mates (5) (p24 and p25)

And so, **Judas** agreed to tell the **angry** leaders where Jesus would be for just **30** pieces of **SILVER**. While Jesus was praying that evening, |soldiers| appeared, *LED* by Judas, and captured him. Then they put him on trial.

"You told me this Jesus was causing **trouble** everywhere. Well, **I've** **? ? ? ?** questioned him, and so has *Herod*, and I don't think he deserves to **DIE** — he's done nothing wrong. I'll have him whipped and that'll be the end of it." But the crowd **SHOUTED**, **"KILL HIM! KILL HIM!"**

The man in charge couldn't quite **believe** what he was hearing. So he told the crowd (again) that Jesus had done nothing wrong. "Kill him! Kill him! Put him on a **CROSS!**

"Crucify him!"

"But **WHY?** He hasn't done anything! I've *TOLD* you,

I'll get him whipped and beaten up — surely that's enough?"

said Pilate. He was getting *pretty desperate*

now. But the **SHOUTING** didn't stop. IN FACT , it

got worse and worse, the crowds were truly **scary**

now, and eventually Pilate **gave in**. "Do what you

WANT with him," he said, as he walked away.

Hidden around this page are some objects that you might find in a modern courtroom when a person is on trial. Can **YOU** find them all?

51

And that's what they did. They crucified JESUS.

(Crucify? (say Croo-si-fy) Crucifixion? (say Croo-si-fic-shun) Essentially, a person who is crucified is fastened on to 2 pieces of wood in the shape of a cross, which is stood up in a hole in the ground, and then they are LEFT there until they DIE. Usually the Romans put BIG STRONG nails through their hands and feet so that the people could not escape.

Join the dots to FIND out where they took Jesus to be crucified and what it looked like.

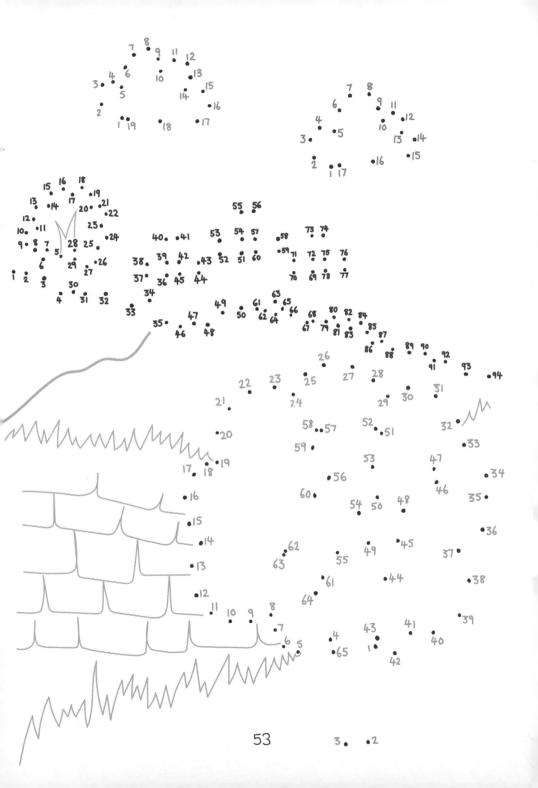

53

At around twelve o'clock **everything** went dark. The sky was black. The sun had stopped shining. Everything stayed **DARK** until the middle of the afternoon, when *suddenly* the curtain in the Temple tore in **TWO** and Jesus shouted out: "Father, into **your** hands I place my spirit."

And then he **DIED**.

But don't **worry**! That's not the end... Because **3 days later** something really, really, really awesome happened... When some of Jesus' friends went to see **WHERE** he'd been buried – **GUESS** what?!

When they arrived, the first thing they **SAW** was the **ENORMOUS** stone that had been put in front of the place where Jesus' body *lay*. It wasn't where it had been **LEFT**. They knew, for sure, that the stone had been in front of the tomb, and now it **wasn't**. It had been rolled away to one side. Odd.

They went **inside**, not knowing what to expect, and Jesus' body wasn't there. They checked everywhere, but the body was definitely  GONE. Freaky.

WOW! WOW! WOW! It wasn't just that Jesus was missing, GOD had brought him back to life!

Colour in the picture to help everyone look as excited and amazed as possible!

Just imagine if you'd been there! It's just so WONDERFUL. He really is God's Son, he's really alive — and he's STILL alive today!

For QUITE a while after Jesus had come back to life again, he kept on hanging out with his mates, just like BEFORE, and teaching them LOTS about GOD. And he was absolutely, 100% real!

Jesus held out his hands and his feet and moved around the room. The disciples just STARED. They were absolutely blown away.

"I'm hungry," Jesus said. "Have you got any food?"

"F-F-F-F-FISH," they managed to say, and passed Jesus a piece to eat. He munched his way through his HUNK of fish while they all just stared at him. Then Jesus said:

"When I was with you BEFORE, I told you

everything that had already been said about me, everything that had to **HAPPEN**. Don't you remember, the writings left behind by God's messengers so *long* **AGO**? They said the Messiah would have to **DIE** and three days *later* he would be **ALIVE** again. They said that people everywhere need to go through **ME** to get to **GOD** so they can be *forgiven*. And that starts **NOW**.

Draw yourself sharing some bread and fish with Jesus — what else might you add to your plate?

This wasn't the END at all; it was just the beginning...

And you KNOW I said I'd come ⟨back⟩ to the whole

doghouse thing? Well, let me explain.

When Jesus **died** on the cross, ✝ it's like he took the dog's

place in the doghouse, so that he could come back inside

and be with YOU again.

When Jesus **died** on the cross, ✝ he was there to take

the punishment for our SIN, so that we could come ⟨back⟩

to GOD and be with him again.

AWESOME - right?

DID YOU KNOW that Christians believe

Luke's story is far **more** than just that... They believe it's all **100%** true. You can read his  sto ry for yourself in a **Bible**, you'll find it listed as 'The Gospel of Luke'.

If you'd like to find out **more** about what Christians believe then visit www.scriptureunion.org.uk or ask at your local CHURCH.

ANSWERS:

P6 & P7

Missing words in order: Doctor; well; sick; awesome; book; two; important; share; world

P8 & P9

P10 & P11

The correct speech bubbles:
• He was born next to animal poo!
• That baby's parents weren't even married!
• He kind of had two dads, you know!
• Someone brought him gold as a present! Wow!
• There was a special star that told people where to find him!

P20 & P21

Missing words in order: carrying; walk; healed; shouting; crowd; tiles; above; man; forgiveness; muttering; amazing

P12 & P13

Answer: His name is JESUS

P22 & P23

P24 & P25

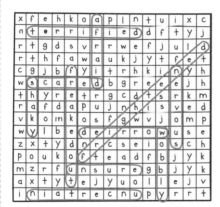

P26 & P27

P28 & P29

Answer: 12

P30 & P31

Philip

Bartholomew

Judas 1

James 2

Simon

John

Peter

Thomas

Andrew

P32 & P33

Answer:
PRAY ABOUT EVERYTHING

P38 & P39

God **really, really** loves you just as you are. There's *NOTHING* you could do to make him love you **MORE** ♡ ⬇

and there's *NOTHING* you could do to make him love you less.

P40 & P41

x	c	f	t	y	j	k	o	p	d	e
k	i	n	d	n	e	s	s	m	g	s
f	r	t	e	a	u	p	o	e	h	s
v	e	z	f	d	g	h	a	k	e
o	a	g	s	h	a	r	i	n	g	n
h	t	f	i	g	h	t	i	n	g	e
k	p	e	c	v	b	e	g	e	u	v
g	i	v	i	n	g	s	l	s	m	i
j	y	o	j	b	u	v	p	s	c	g
l	t	l	c	e	s	x	h	s	e	r
e	c	n	e	i	t	a	p	v	x	o
f	j	t	y	u	i	s	e	k	l	f

Good fruit   Bad fruit

P46 & P47

(The Passo-*WHAT*? Passover is a Jewish festival. So every **Jew** in **J**erusalem would've been getting ready to celebrate it. They'd been **celebrating** Passover for hundreds and hundreds of years by having a special meal that reminded them of when their very **ancient** family was set free from **E**gypt. You can read all about it in the **Bible**, if you have one – have a look at **Exodus chapter 12**.)

P42 & P43

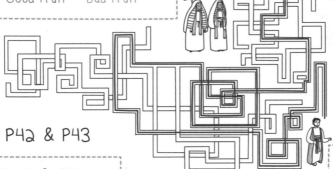

START

P44 & P45

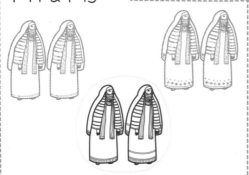

P48 & P49

Crossword answers:
1. fish
2. twelve
3. wine
4. matthew
5. passover
6. james
7. trouble
8. body
9. bread
10. storm